havin it
large

Kevin & Perry's guide
to looking cool and getting girls

richard topping

B⊞XTREE

For Ian, Clive, Geoff, Roy, Dipak and Nigel.
Good thinking lads.

First published 2000 by Boxtree
an imprint of Macmillan Publishers Ltd
25 Eccleston Place London SW1W 9NF
Basingstoke and Oxford

www.macmillan.co.uk

Associated companies throughout the world

ISBN 0 7522 7188 1

1 3 5 7 9 8 6 4 2

A CIP catalogue record for this book is available from the British Library.

All photographs by Stephen Vaughan, © Tiger Aspect Pictures 2000 except the following:
Hulton Getty: 104–105; Tony Stone Images: 12–15, 98, 102–103;
Richard Topping: 39, 41, 51–56, 79, 100–101, 119–121.

Illustrations on pages 30–31, 65–69 by Debbie Hinks;
illustrations on pages 72–73, 115–117, 123 by Dan Newman.

Designed by Blackjacks

Printed by The Bath Press

NOTE: None of the recipes or ingredients in this book
is intended for human or animal consumption.

contents

1

havin' it large

Being fifteen is cosmic punishment for being superior to everyone on the entire planet, especially because anyone older – as any fifteen-year-old will tell you – is stupid and doesn't know anything. If we had our way, when you got to fifteen you'd automatically become Prime Minister (as long as you could use your decks properly) and all the civil servants and MPs would be hot ladies in swimsuits who hadn't had any for months. Alas, it doesn't work like that.

It's like this. You're *sooooooo* up for a shag, but girls won't look at you without laughing. You *sooooooo* know how to make thumpin' choons but no-one takes you seriously. You're *sooooooo* up for a monster raving rave-fest in Ibiza, but you've got no money and your parents insist on coming just so they can ruin it for you. It's *sooooooo* unfair!

So what do you do?

Easy Peasy Lemon Squeezy. Read our book.

Between the covers of this massively best-selling work of genius we've crammed a lifetime of Havin' It Large experience. It's the kind of experience money just can't buy. Well, actually you have bought it, but you know what we're saying. Want advice on how to chat up a lady? We've chatted up *loads!* Want experience on choons? We're top-selling DJs! Want experience on getting a shag? We've shagged loads more than someone who hasn't... um... shagged at all.

We're monsta ravin' mega mixers, rinsin' love machines who want to help anyone – even old people in their twenties – have it as large as we do.

We're Kevin and Perry.
You're sorted.

Innit!

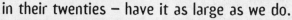
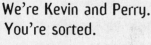

how large

Not everyone has what it takes to become as cool as we are. Like Jafaar says in 'Aladdin', 'Are you a diamond in the rough?'. Or it might be 'Are you a bit of rough?'. Either way, there's no point you even looking any further unless you've got a good grounding in Innitism.

A word of warning though – if you fail the test, don't buy this book. Don't even look at it. And if you've already bought it, give it to someone who's cooler than you are. Me and Perry are a bit particular about who we share our secrets with. If you break the rules, we'll send round our best mate Big Baz, who used to be a bouncer at Amnesia. That means he's quite tough actually, so watch it.

Circle all your answers with a sharp, HB pencil. If you make a mistake, erase your first answer and enter a second choice. No conferring and no turning the book upside down to peep at the answers. You have one minute, starting from... NOW!

A Double Decker is...?

A A big bus with steps going upstairs where you can sit at the back and swear at old ladies

B A nice chocolate and crunchy/chewy nougat candy bar in an orange wrapper

C A record deck with two turntables used for mixing rinsin' choons

A Puffa is...?

A A heavy smoker

B A jacket

C A homemade cigarette with a cardboard insert and a funny smell

If someone says 'You're a great mixer,' what do they mean?

A You're a class act on the turntables

B You like talking to people at parties, amusing them with your witty anecdotes and seamless social skills

C You go quite well with Gin

Fatboy Slim is...?

A A make of cigar

B A diet

C Really called Norman

Have you ever referred to a rave as a 'disco'?

A Yes

B No

C What's a 'rave'?

The Ministry of Sound is...?

A A government department that has something to do with stopping noisy parties

B A multi-million pound club and music franchise

C A well-sorted religion

question 7

Parents are...?

A The people who gave you life

B Your link with the past

C Fascists

question 8

Are you a virgin?

A Yes

B Yes

C Yes

question 9

Are Kevin and Perry your mentors and spiritual guides?

A Yes

B No

C Er... what was the question again?

question 10

If it takes three men four hours to dig a hole six foot deep, how long would it take two men to dig a hole five foot deep?

A Four hours

B Five hours

C Six hours

thumpin' or chumpin'?

So, how did you do? Add up your scores and find out if you're a happenin' dude or a hapless dodo.

0-15 *Oh dear. Let's face it, this book's gonna be about as much use to you as a porno mag during Sunday lunch round your granny's. Give up now and go home. If you're already at home, go somewhere else, but don't take our book with you. You're pathetic. You make us sick. Look, I just vomited all over Perry, that's how sick I am. You're so uncool you'll probably drop dead from an uncool attack any minute now. You'd better call an ambulance before it's too late.*

16-23 *Well, it's not exactly brilliant, but I suppose you've gotta start somewhere. Most of this book will be a bit of an effort, I mean you won't even understand the basics, but we're gonna give you a second chance cos we're generous like that. But mess up once – JUST ONCE – and you're out, alright? And brush your teeth, your breath smells.*

24-27 *Whey Hey! Bombs away. You're all set to soak up our years of experience. You're chooned in and chilled out. You're up with it and down in it. This book's made for you. Take a chapter at a time, memorise key passages and remember, although sometimes it'll be hard work, the effort is all worth it. We're gonna make you RINSIN'! And if you haven't had a shag by the time you've got to the end, you're probably reading too quickly.*

28 *Yeah, alright smart arse. Just remember whose book it is, alright?*

gettin' cool

2

There's some stupid advert that says image is nothing. Rubbish. Image is everything. I mean, if you go around dressed in the sort of rags your mother buys you from C&A you'll never get a shag. In the cut-throat world of getting your leg over, image is king.

But bein' cool isn't just about what you wear. It's about how you communicate with other rinsin' ravers, using the universal language of pointing and waving your arms about. In this – the second chapter in our Bible of Being Blindin' – we're gonna show you what to wear, what NOT to wear (take one look at your own parents, there's a giveaway) and how to get across vital information in the heady, crazy, thumpin' clubs that are your spiritual home.

Monsta!

lookin' good

SCOUSE BLOUSE £2.50

If you've got a gormless mentality, you'll want a gormless T-shirt to go with it. We model these super cheap 'n' nasty tops from Scouse that will disintegrate after the first wash and make all your other clothes go dark blue. Available from most market stalls.

ROMFORD SLACKS £38.90

They say if you put a shell suit to your ear, you can hear Romford! We show you how a well-cut pair of tracksuit bottoms can evoke

FLUFFY BUNNY £12.99

Here Candice shows that – even when you've got a face like a bulldog chewing a wasp – a vibrant colour and a great texture can be perfect for diverting attention away from your ugly mug.

PETROL PUMPS £19.99

Been ram raiding? Need to get away swift as possible? Whether you're a juvenile delinquent or not, these stylish yet practical shoes are perfect for legging it when things go arse up. Available in three colours.

PONCEY SHIRTS £1.56

If the Scouse range of T-shirts isn't cheap 'n' nasty enough for you, here Perry models a budget top that will actually stain your skin bright red if you get caught in the rain.

BORED WHERE? JACKET £12.99

Perry shows us how easy it is to transform yourself from harmless teenager to skateboarding demon. Ideal for cold afternoons spent scratching cars in Waitrose car park and frightening old ladies and small children. What a bargain at £12.99!

SPICE GIRLS – OFF THE RACK £10.99 – £50.00

Here Candice and Gemma show how easy it is to look like a couple of right old scrubbers who'll put out at the drop of a hat. Low slung dockers are ideal for showing your septic belly button ring and – if you've got any – a few tufts of pubic hair poking out the top.

KRAPPY JUMPER £49.99

Not to everyone's taste, the Krappy jumper sports extra-long sleeves and sloping shoulders – perfect for sulking or waving your arms about after a meaningless parental argument.

PANTS PANTS £35.99

Here Kevin demonstrates the special stiffy-fit baggy crotch cut – essential for walking whilst parading a towering stiffy. Note the extra depth pockets, for discrete but essential fiddling.

NOT
lookin' good

Stupid hat!

Ooh, look, it's the man from Del Monte. Or is that the man from El Crappo?

Marks & Spencer blouse. Brilliant for old ladies.

Shirt tucked into trousers. You saddo!

Long skirts. Dur! Good for keeping ugly old legs covered up!

Trying very hard to look like Noel Gallagher. Actually looks like Noel Edmonds.

Look – no pockets. Look – no brain!

Sandals! AND SOCKS! It doesn't get much worse than this. I think I'm going to vomit.

'The Clubber's Choice'

Dead Bull

STIMULATION FOR THE STIFFY

Dead Bull Gives You The Horn

*i*f you want conversation, hang around McDonalds with your mates. Or in the park, as long as it's not raining. But when it comes to clubbin', there's no point trying to talk to anyone cos they won't hear a word you're saying. (And you're probably so boring they wouldn't want to listen to you anyway.) But sometimes, it's essential to get something communicated when you're largin' it up. Lucky for you, we've developed a unique and brilliant way of making yourself understood *through the power of dance!* Wicked!

It is THIS unfair!

Yeah!

…less!

I've got a stiffy this big.

Actually, I've seen it – and it's no bigger than this.

I hate my parents THIS much.

I fancy his mum THIS much.

personal
grooming

3

"For some reason, ladies get really stroppy if you haven't cleaned your teeth before you stick your tongue down their throats. As stupid and picky as this may sound, it's worth bearing in mind if you're planning on getting shagged while you're on holiday.

Other bits that upset them are armpits, feet, and chuffy bottoms. In this, a chapter near the beginning of the book, we're gonna look at various grooming tips that will help you get all nice and clean, ready for that big moment when she puts her hand inside your dockers.

Mmmm...

Erm... excuse me, I just need to go to the bathroom."

bathroom time

Ever wondered what we do in the bathroom for hours on end, even though we still come out smelly and all the hot water's gone? Well, I'm not really supposed to let on, it bein' a teenage secret and all that, but given you've got this far, you might as well know the truth.

Oi Perry you plonk! It's a secret!! I'll scrub it out before Mum sees it

First we fill the bath ▓▓ cheesy ▓▓▓▓▓▓▓▓▓▓▓▓▓▓▓▓▓ sticky ▓▓▓▓▓▓▓▓▓▓▓▓▓▓▓▓▓▓▓▓▓▓▓▓▓▓▓▓▓▓▓▓▓▓▓▓▓▓▓ and using the sponge ▓▓▓ once it's stopped bleeding ▓▓▓▓▓▓▓▓▓▓▓▓▓▓▓▓▓▓

26

but not in the sink

badly stained

trousers get in the way.

hair goes crunchy

crusty

Once it's dry you pull f

apparatus

fill the bath again,

but this time a s.

feel lovely

and then you can put them back on again.

face like a
dog's
arse?

Bein' beautiful ain't easy, innit. Me and Gemma, wot are top models, and not monsters, we came up wiv some makeover tips for girls wot might need a hand lookin' brilliant.

face

Some people get zits, wot are 'orrible. Give 'em a good squeeze before you go out, but be careful. We've done a special page on zits, cos they're tricky innit.

nose hair

Bushy nostrils ain't very nice. They get caught in the umbrella in your cocktails, and make a shadow on your lip when you're sunbathing. You can pull 'em out with some pliers, which hurts loads. Or you can get some garden shears, wot are really tough scissors, and snip 'em on the inside. Don't cut your nose off though, cos that'll look worse.

legs

Legs wot are hairy are manky. They poke out of your tights and look like squashed flies. First, cut off the tufts wiv the shears (wot you've used for the nostrils) and then shave them with your Dad's razor. Don't bother washin' it out, cos it'll be ruined anyway.

furry muff

Havin' spider's legs poke out your bikini makes you look disgustin'. No-one likes a pant 'tache, so you need to do your 'bikini line' wiv some industrial strength Elephant tape. Stick it to your furry bits, and get a mate to yank it off really hard. It might hurt a bit, especially if the skin comes wiv it.

feet

Some girls have hard lumpy bits on their feet, which are alright unless some boy wants to suck them like Fergie's bald bloke did. Get rid of 'em wiv a cheese grater, wot you can use to whittle your feet down 'til they're lovely.

armpits

Only froggy garlic munchers 'ave hairy pits, so get 'em shaved. Better if you use your Dad's electric razor, wot is better for sweaty places.

Zit pickers

Me and Candice get zits, and know what to do wiv 'em right, cos they're manky int they? Here's some squeezy zit tips.

WHITEHEAD

Dead easy to pick on the quiet, innit. Quick scrape wiv the fingernail and it's gone. Bit sneaky these ones cos they can appear real quick. Get on the bus – none. Get off the bus – your nose is full of 'em.

CLASSIC PIMPLE

This one's what we get all the time in the morning, yeah. Bit pointy, wiv a squeeze hole on the top. Fingers wide apart. Press firmly. It ain't finished 'til that hard bit comes out the end, like a little worm innit.

CLASSIC MOUNTAIN RANGE

These are 'orrible, int they?
Zit on a zit on a family of zits.
Start at the foothills and squeeze
upwards. Use cotton wool and
stop when you see blood. That
means your face is gonna fall
off, like that Elephant Man.

VESUVIUS

Yuck. You'll need
lots of white spirit
for this, like wot to
clean the mirror wiv
cos it's so septic.

THE GOLF BALL

Whatever you do, never squeeze
a golf ball. It's right down deep
innit and there's no 'ead on it.
It hurts like 'ell and never splats.
If you squeeze it, it just goes
purple. DO NOT TOUCH!

Stiffy Diary

When it comes to the crunch, you wanna be sure your stiffy's up to the challenge. They can be pretty unpredictable at the best of times, so try keepin' a stiffy diary to work out when you're at your peak. Then draw a graph so you can work out when's the best time to cop off.

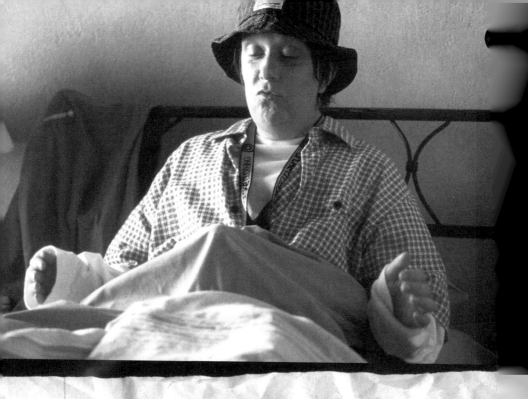

24 Hours in Perry's Pants - a diary

LOCATION	REASON	DURATION
On the plane	Saw stewardess's boobies	Entire flight
On the runway	Warm breeze	Fifteen minutes
In the hire car	Bounced around a bit	Half an hour
On the beach	Bums. Boobies. Legs. Mmm...	'Til I got back to the apartment
At the club	Bums. Boobies. Legs. Mmm...	'Til I went to the bathroom
Having dinner	Don't know	On and off for three hours
In the apartment	Saw Mrs Patterson's bra	Two and a half hours
In the morning	Morning!	'Til I had a shower
Having breakfast	Nice muffins	Ten minutes
Shops	Girl in the shop	All day
Gent's loo	How did that happen?	Don't want to talk about it
Outside Mr & Mrs P's bedroom	Saw Mr P givin' it large to Mrs P	4.5 seconds

problem page

Got a problem? Write to Kev and Pel, who pretty much know everything. We'll give you tip top advice – in complete confidence!

Dear Kev and Pel
I keep getting stiffies at awkward moments. In the showers. On the beach. Standing at the bus-stop. Sitting on the bus. Actually, I pretty much have a stiffy all the time. What can I do?
Ian Ramsey
Class 4b, Westbury Secondary School

Stop worrying about it. Me and Pel get stiffies all the time. We love 'em! Wear your stiffy with pride. Tell the world, I'm up, and up for it! Wear the baggiest trousers you can and show everyone what a real stiffy looks like. After all – it's what separates the men from the boys! KP

star letter

Dear Kev and Pel
I have a teenage son who is driving me mad. He's rude, argumentative, intolerant, aggressive, and quite frankly I'm close to throttling the little shit. Any advice?
Mr Patterson, Surbiton

Mr Patterson – It's obviously all your fault. If you weren't so old and stupid, you'd realise what a tortured genius your son is and how your perpetual harassment is so unfair. Leave him alone and stop being such a Hitler. Oh, and give him more pocket money. Then he can go out more and leave you alone. KP

Dear Kev and Pel
My teenage son and my husband fight night and day. I love them both but I'm caught in the middle and I don't know what to do. Any advice?
Mrs Patterson, Surbiton

Dear Mrs P – Here's an idea. Why not get off with your son's best mate? He probably thinks you're a bit of alright, and no-one'll ever know. As for your husband – he's too old to give it to you proper, and teenagers have got much more stamina, innit. Large! PF

4

lovin' the ladies

Before you go away to Ibiza to get your first shag – which is almost definitely the only reason for going – you need to know how to impress the ladies. That means you need to *understand* the ladies. Me and Perry have assembled some of our best tips on how you might do this.

Since you passed 'the knowledge' at the beginning of this book, we're confident that you have enough responsibility and maturity to handle this dynamite information. But be careful. If it gets into the wrong hands it could cause chaos the world over. It's the sexual equivalent of giving a ~~kalashn,~~ ~~kalashnek,~~ ~~kaleshni~~ really big gun to a tiny little kid.

We've covered everything here, from your basic chat-up lines ('Oooh Candice, lick my love plank'), to what cocktails you should mix them when you get back to your flat and they're gasping for a big one.

Here's a few golden rules.

★ Be yourself
★ If you can't be yourself, be someone else. Pierce Brosnan or Liam Gallagher might be a good choice.
★ Always treat the ladies with respek
★ Always naff off when they tell you
★ Don't let them see you following them

Now it's up to you...

where it's at

The worst thing about being an explorer is that you don't have a map. Obviously. Otherwise you wouldn't be an explorer, would you? It's the same with girls. The worst thing about discovering what girls' bodies are like is that you've never been there before. Well, we have. But you probably haven't.

The first step is to get hold of a good porno mag (see later this chapter). This'll show you where all the er... bits and pieces are. But once you've got the rudiments sorted out, you need to check your progress.

Me and Perry have put together this Shagometer, using one of Perry's sister's dolls. We've painted all the really important bits different colours, and given them points. Depending on how far you can grope during a snog, the idea is to get as big a score as possible. Or any score at all, actually.

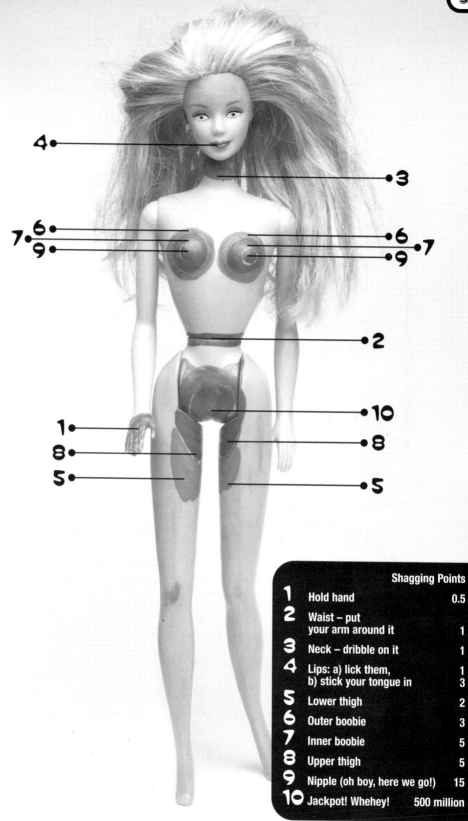

	Shagging Points	
1	Hold hand	0.5
2	Waist – put your arm around it	1
3	Neck – dribble on it	1
4	Lips: a) lick them, b) stick your tongue in	1 3
5	Lower thigh	2
6	Outer boobie	3
7	Inner boobie	5
8	Upper thigh	5
9	Nipple (oh boy, here we go!)	15
10	Jackpot! Whehey!	500 million

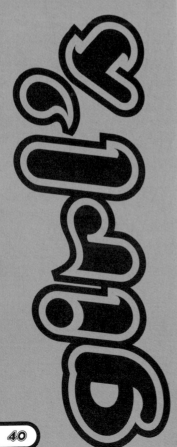

Me and Gemma thought that last bit was really sexy. Erm, no, sorry, <u>sexist</u>. So we're gonna 'ave a word or two about boys, wot are disgusting, innit.

The reason most girls don't let boys go all the way is cos most boys are stinky. When they're not dribbling in your ear they're trying to get their grubby hands in your knickers – which is 'orrible of them.

While the boys are adding up all their stupid points on their Shagometer, girls should add up their own points on the Stinkometer, wot we made out of a toy my brother lent me.

Every time you get a whiff, use the Stinkometer to keep score. If you get to 40 Stinkypoints, chuck 'em. Oh wot the hell, chuck 'em after 10.

		Stinky Points
1	Armpits	3
2	Feet	5
3	Breath	7
4	Arse (when it chuffs)	100
5	Sweaty crotch (yukko!)	100 million

PORN ON THE 4TH OF JULY

It was the height of summer, and Kev and Pel had the raging horn.

All tooled up with a bag of cash, insatiable curiosity and majestic stiffies, they made a trip to Mr Patel's on the corner.

This is their story.

Kevin, pumped to the brim with testosterone and adrenalin, makes the first move – the reach 'n' grab.

Bloody hell. I'm minutes away from having my own brand new porno mag. What if I get caught?

continued over

In the ensuing madness, the bag rips open and 'XXX Porno Lust Bunnies' spill onto the pavement just as Mr Patterson sees the boys.

Kevin! Are you alright?

Uh-oh... Stiffy!

Kevin makes the ultimate sacrifice and throws himself over the explosive contents.

Yes thank you Dad. I'm a bit tired – just having a lie-down.

Phew! Lucky escape lads! More pornography-inspired japes next week.

THE END

CHAT-UPS

the pre-chat-up

Before you actually chat 'up' a lady, it's a good idea to chat 'around' the lady, just so she can get interested in you and find out – simply by overhearing your conversation – what a lovely, sensitive and utterly shagworthy person you are.

To this end, first you need to strike up a natural pose somewhere near the ladies in question. You need to be close enough for them to hear you, but not so close that they can feel your stiffies.

Then launch into one of the set-conversations detailed below. This is how me and Perry do it.

small fluffy animals

Perry: *I say Kevin, what's it like being really famous and everything?*

Kevin: *What, you mean after winning that Nobel Prize for Services to Small Fluffy Animals, wot are cute?*

Perry: *That is right Kevin.*

Kevin: *It's great, except I wish to meet a special girl who understands me and doesn't just want to shag me because I have saved so many small and fluffy animals from a horrible death.*

Perry: *Where would you find such a girl Kevin?*

Kevin: *In heaven, Perry, only in heaven.*

giggin' at glastonbury

Kevin: So tell me Perry, what did happen at Glastonbury exactly?

Perry: Well Kevin, as you know I was about to play my set when Fatboy Slim...

Kevin: ...whose real name is Norman Cook, I think you will find Perry.

Perry: That is correct Kevin, whose real name is Norman Cook, came up to me and said 'Perry, I had such a hard night last night that I completely forgot all my decks and all my records and all my choons this morning. Could I borrow yours?'

Kevin: And you said?

Perry: 'Not again Norman. That's the third time this week. Never again!'

Kevin: How nice of you to be so nice, Perry.

Perry: Indeed Kevin. But none of the girls I shag at concerts appreciate me for being so nice. They just want me because I am such a good lover – as well as a DJ who lends his records to Fatboy Slim.

big willy

Perry: It's a tragedy Kevin. A tragedy that the doctors can do nothing about you having such an enormous thingie.

Kevin: I am devastated Perry. It is an embarrassment to be so enormous, so fantastically huge that doctors from all over the world have flown to England to work out how I could have one so big.

Perry: And so tragic that they cannot make it smaller.

Kevin: Tragic.

the chat-up

Once you have laid all the groundwork using the chat-around conversations above, it's time to do the chat-up itself. These ones nearly always work.

Kevin: Suck my candy!
Perry: Lick my love plank!

the post-chat-up

Sometimes, after the chat-up, you will need a back-up conversation for anyone who might have been watching you try the chat-up.

Perry: Ho ho ho Kevin! It is so funny how our girlfriends always kick us in the goolies when they are having a laugh with us!

Kevin: Yes Perry. Our girl-friends have a right giggle by slapping us in the faces. What a good laugh they are!

Perry: Ha! Ha! Ha!

Mix-ma-stas!

Not knowing how to mix the ladies a drink when you invite them back to your love shack can be almost as catastrophic as your Mum kissing you in public. So here s some of our home-made secret cocktail recipes* which are guaranteed to get you your first shag. Unless you drink one yourself of course.

This exciting range of cocktails has never been seen anywhere before. We have avoided traditional ingredients, choosing instead to use ones not normally found in a club bar. Me and Perry got the job of feeding gran s cat when she went into hospital to have her hip operation and this was what she had in her drinks cupboard. And in her medicine cabinet. And in her shed.

* see page ii

Silver Lady

1 part Gripewater
6 parts Lemonade

Pour the gripewater into a cocktail glass and fill to the top with the lemonade (careful, it goes a bit frothy). Stir gently, add a piece of lime on a stick and an umbrella.

Kevin – these drinks are stupid + irresponsible – drink any of these and you ARE NOT GOING ON HOLIDAY!
Mum

GRIPE WATER
ALCOHOL & SUGAR FREE

lemonade
330 ml

VERDICT
Kev: 'One for the ladies!'

VERDICT
Pel: 'Nice and minty!'

Chunky-Spunky-Munky

3 parts Energy drink
1 part Apricot brandy
1 part Real Ale
1 part Chicken soup

Mix the energy drink and brandy first, then top up with the Real ale and soup. Then spoon in a few chopped carrots. This gives it a nice orangey effect, and also means you have something to chew on to take away the taste of the drink.

VERDICT

Kev: 'Great colour. Tastes a bit pukey though!'

VERDICT

Pel: 'Smells like my stiffy. Hur, Hur!'

Flemmie Cough Splut

1 part chilled Advocaat
3 parts cough mixture

Pour the chilled Advocaat in a glass, then drizzle in the cough mixture so it makes nice swirly patterns. Then stick some fruit in it. That'll make it look good.

VERDICT

Kev: 'Mmm... nice if you've got a frog in your throat.

VERDICT

Pel: 'I quite like it. Is my tongue purple?'

Balearic Barf

2 parts fizzy tropical drink
1 part Red wine

Pour in the red wine (we couldn't find any, so we used red wine vinegar instead. Wish we hadn't.) Then add twice as much fizzy tropical drink. Stick a few cherries round the top. Serve in a very small glass. It helps if you hold your nose when you drink it.

VERDICT

Kev: 'Smells like cat piss!'

VERDICT

Pel: 'I'm feeling a bit sick!'

fizzy tropical drink

Red Wine Vinegar

FOR SALAD DRESSINGS
SAUCES AND MARINADES

Chocolate Monsta

1 part Calvados
2 parts Sherry
Mix the ingredients together then decorate with an apple and grate chocolate over the top. If you can't find real chocolate, use my gran's favourite, Laxchoc.

VERDICT

Kev: 'I can't drink this very well. The apple keeps getting stuck in my eye. Hey, Perry. Guess what? This drink's the apple of my eye. Ha!'

VERDICT

Pel: 'I really need to go to the toilet Kevin. Are you listening? Kevin? Kev? Wake up!'

Red Devil

1 part Vodka

1 red felt tip pen (for colour)

Pour in the vodka. Stick a pen in it. Or is that two pens? Can't seem to focus properly. Looks nice though.

VERDICT

Kev: 'Urrrgghhhhghghh!' (splash)

VERDICT

Pel: No verdict, he's still in the toilet.

the joy of seduction

(actually, not getting any)

Getting into a girl's knickers is harder than getting tickets to Fatboy Slim's Brighton Millennium Party. And the problem is, you never know if they actually want it or not. When they do, they pretend they don't. When they don't, they pretend they do. If you guess wrong, you'll get slapped and never lose your virginity.

So what me and Kev have done is spend ages trying to get off with girls, and reported back on what works and what doesn't.

Mostly, nothing works. But here's a few smooth moves that might get you started. Or arrested.

scenario 1 – watching TV on the sofa

the yawn 'n' grab

- Position yourself as near to your lady as you can possibly be, without actually sitting on her lap.
- Yawn theatrically. Make sure you've cleaned your teeth well or the resulting guff of bad breath could force her off the sofa.
- Raise both arms above your head as the yawn reaches its peak (anatomically, a yawn uses similar processes to an orgasm. Concentrate hard or this may be as close as you get...).
- End the yawn by lowering the arm nearest to your lady onto the sofa behind her.
- Now lean forward to get the TV control. Your arm will automatically slide onto her shoulders.

The rebuff
- If she's not up for it, the moment your arm touches her shoulder, she'll get up and go to the toilet. When she comes back, she'll sit on the other end of the sofa.

The counter rebuff
- Get up and go to the toilet yourself (you may well need to anyway).
- Come back and sit next to her.
- Start again.
- This can go on for hours. Days sometimes.

the snog

- Breathe heavily in her ear.
- Kick the cat on your side of the sofa.
- When she turns around to see what the noise is, stick your tongue in.

The rebuff
- A slap.

The counter rebuff
- Give up. There isn't one. Go home and watch *Baywatch* (make sure Mum's not in).

the boobie prize

(only to be executed after the Yawn 'n' Grab)
- ▶ Now your arm's on her shoulder, use every shift in either your position or hers to allow your hand to 'slip' further and further down towards (gulp) her boobie. Unless you want to strangle her, this will actually involve you having to stretch hugely uncomfortable distances.
- ▶ Remember your mission objective. To get to that little lumpy bit (mmmm...).

The rebuff
- ▶ She'll grab hold of your hand and move it back up to her shoulder. But you know she wants it...

The counter rebuff
- ▶ Each time your hands gets moved back, make sure you get further next time.

The counter-counter rebuff
- ▶ A slap.

The counter-counter-counter rebuff
- ▶ Once again, there isn't one. You're not much good at this are you?

the knee clutch

This one's always worth a pop if you've just suffered the Boobie Prize counter-counter rebuff.
- ▶ Put your hand on her knee.
- ▶ Each time you lean forward to (i) eat crisps (ii) change channels (iii) do nothing in particular, allow your hand to slide further up her thigh.

The rebuff
- ▶ She'll grab hold of your hand and move it back down to her knee. But you still think she wants it...

The counter rebuff
- ▶ Each time your hand gets moved back, make sure you get further next time.

The counter-counter rebuff
- ▶ A slap.

The counter-counter-counter rebuff
- ▶ Fake a heart attack. Maybe she'll give you mouth-to-mouth.

scenario 2 – at the club

the disco diggler

- ▶ Find your target.
- ▶ Try to stay inconspicuous and dance up behind her. If she's seen you, this might actually reduce your chances.
- ▶ Make no attempt to hide your stiffy.
- ▶ Nuzzle yourself into the small of her back.
- ▶ Wait and see what happens. Which is usually...

The rebuff
- ▶ A screech of disgust.
- ▶ A slap.

The counter rebuff
- ▶ Move on to her mate and give it another go.

the slow grope

If the Disco Diggler has been successful, come the smooch at the end, you're in a brilliant position to really cop off.
- ▶ Put both hands on her back, one high, one low.
- ▶ Now move the lower one even lower. And lower. And lower.

The rebuff
- ▶ She'll go home. Without you.

The counter rebuff
- ▶ Er... there isn't one. Go home and polish some soap.

Girls like bods which are all muscley, firm and suntanned, and not white, flabby and saggy. Not only that, dancing in a club all night takes a lot of energy and unless you're in tippity-tip-top condition, you might get out of breath quite a lot. And then when you come to snog a girl you'll collapse, which is embarrassing.

So how can you get in shape before you go on holiday, thus ensuring your chances of going-all-the-way with a girl who thinks you have a six-pack like that tall one out of Five?

Easy! Do the regular exercises me and Perry use to keep in shape. This is our work-out:

getting in shape

warm-up

Lie on the sofa watching the TV for three hours pressing the change-channel button every few seconds and going 'Grrr! Hur! Grr! Hur!' in disgust cos there's nothing on. This is quite hard work and might make you hungry, in which case a pot noodle or a packet of chocolate hobnobs are good energy boosters. Do not interrupt your work-out to get these yourself. The words 'Mum – I'm HUNGRY!' can be neatly fitted into your exercise routine and can build up those all-essential jaw muscles so you'll look even more like Fatboy Slim (whose real name is Norman Cook I think you'll find).

the mope

When your mother refuses to get you anything – because she is old and decrepit and hates you – get off the sofa and walk in and out of the kitchen with your head down, waving your arms at knee level. This is very hard work and so to get your breathing right, repeat the phrase 'Dur! Sooooo UNFAIR!' over and over and over.

the stairclimber

Now stomp up the stairs as fast as you can, almost stamping hard enough to crash your trainers through the steps. This is an excellent lower-body work-out, but unless it is balanced by an upper-body work-out, your frame will look strangely mismatched and out of proportion, something you never see in teenagers.

the door slammer

In order to balance up your muscles, do this upper-body work-out. Go to the bathroom and slam the door as hard as you can. Try to get plaster dust falling from the ceiling.

polishing

Once in the bathroom, you have an ideal opportunity to build up the muscles in your wrist and forearm. Try polishing a bar of soap – perhaps while flicking through *XXX Porno Lust Bunnies.*

the wader

Now the really tough one. Get some food and go to your bedroom. You have to make it across your room to the bed, where you can eat the food and then stuff the dirty dish on top of the wardrobe (you can do some great stretching exercises retrieving this in six months' time). This means wading through all the clothes. If your room is a genuine expression of free-spirited creativity and non-conformity, everything you own will be artistically piled up on the floor to chest height. Wading through this to the bed is very hard work, but will make you look very athletic once you hit the beach at Ibiza.

breather

Go out onto the landing and listen to see if there is any reaction from your fascist parents, who might shout at you from downstairs. This is a good opportunity to catch your breath. If you get no reaction, repeat the entire work-out, starting at 'Mum – I'm HUNGRY!'.

BETTER
MID-MARRIAGE
SEX

FANNING THE FIRES
OF THE OVER-FORTIES

MR & MRS PATTERSON

CHAPTER
ONE

There comes a time in every marriage – no matter how successful – when the passion and excitement of marital sex begins to
wane. The reasons are numerous; long-term familiarity, less
sexual confidence in our ageing bodies, the pressures of dealing
with teenage children or just good old-fashioned boredom.

We wrote this book – *Better Mid-Marriage Sex* – after redis-
covering the passion of our youth whilst on holiday in Ibiza. It
was while we were removed from our everyday life that we
realised it was possible to rekindle the flame of deep sexual
satisfaction even after many years of marriage. We are not
professional 'sex experts' or therapists. Rather, we're just an
ordinary couple – probably just like you – who want to share the
secret of our erotic reinvention.

Creating the right atmosphere

One of the great barriers preventing a fulfilling sex life is the intrusive presence of children, particularly teenagers who demand that you are there for them at any time of the night or day. The friction caused by disagreements with adolescents can often rub off onto your own relationship with your partner.

If you want to enjoy a night of unrestrained wild sex, create an atmosphere where you won't be disturbed – either by a call from the office or a temper tantrum from the teenager. That means packing the children off somewhere. Not just to their room, but to their granny's, a friend's or ideally another country.

Making time for each other

When you get to your forties, rushed sex is usually bad sex. And in a world where we all lead increasingly busy lives, it's important to schedule time for each other. It may sound unromantic, but set aside time for love. Clear an evening in both your diaries and make a real effort to enjoy a relaxing bath or massage together.

It's important that you're confident of not being disturbed. Close the windows, lock the doors and make sure none of your children's friends is due to pop round for a visit.

Being tender

In the privacy of your own bedroom, tenderness can take any form you like. There's no rules about what you can or cannot do, and since what happens between the two of you will go no further than the bedroom walls, try being adventurous with your affection.

Sometimes couples feel that sex has to be like it is in pornographic movies. Just be yourselves and stop trying to play up to an imaginary camera.

DAD YOU SICKO!!

Experimenting

To put a little sparkle into your sex life, try some mild bondage, such as tying each other up or using a pair of handcuffs. Set the rules before you begin and just be yourselves. No-one's watching!

Making love

Wouldn't the world be boring if everyone made love in the same way! Try different positions, for both his and her enjoyment, and remember that just because you're in your forties, it doesn't mean you can't enjoy the excitement and passion of intimate, orgasmic sex!

knowin' the scene

5

introduction

Some people go to Ibiza when they're just not ready for it – underage, spoddy kids desperate for a shag and completely clueless when it comes to bein' cool and knowin' the scene. Ha! In one way you feel a bit sorry for 'em – me and Kev did – but in another way, it's not really their fault, is it? I mean, we're quite lucky bein' monsta talented deckmeisters and all that. Luckily, me and Kev are dead generous with our experience, and instead of going to clubs and dealing in **DEATH DRUGS**, me and Kev mingle with the people and deal good vibes, cool choons, and super steps.

Let's face it, Ibiza's the Olympics of Largin' It. You could end up with a gold medal in the 100 metres Bangin' It Out Sprint, which is what me and Kev got. Or you could come last, like some saddo ex-DJ we won't mention. So if you wanna stand on the top step with the medal round your neck singing the National Anthem (Big Girl! Big Girl!), listen up. We will say this only once! (But you could record it if you want, we don't mind.)

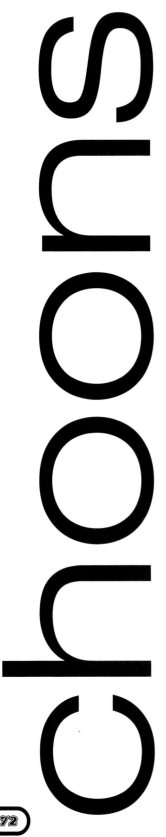

 ## garage
One of the little known facts about Garage is that it was actually invented by nutty ska-band Madness with their hit single 'I Like Driving In My Car' (Diddle Iddle Eep! Beep!). Then monsta Garage band *Mike and The Mechanics* developed its unique sound and it was rapidly adopted by ravers during the early Eighties. Its distinctive noise is a bit like someone dropping a spanner set on a concrete floor over and over again. And over and over again. And over and over again. In early 'Garage' days the familiar bass line was created by Mike Aitken (of Stock, Aitken and Waterman) thumping an oil drum, probably with a garlic crusher. Or a video cassette.

 ## house
House music started in the mid-Eighties at The Pink Flamingo, a now-disused dance club at the end of the pier in Southend-On-Sea. The 'house' DJ, Dave 'Disco' Durridge used to put on Kraftwerk remixes of old Louis Armstrong songs when he went for his evening dump. Because this usually took about an hour and a half, he had to make sure the songs were long enough to cope with his extended bowel movements. It soon became known as 'house music'. The rest is proctology.

 ## acid house
Amongst his other problems, Dave 'Disco' Durridge suffered from really bad indigestion. When he got a particularly nasty attack,

he'd put on one of his 'Acid Stomach House Music' remixes, which usually
lasted over four hours. It's only by chance we don't refer to this as 'Tums House'.

pumping house
The sound coming from Disco Dave's toilet cubicle.

handbag house
There's a club in London where men dress up like ladies
(apparently). They play a lot of house music, but with Abba
samples in them. This is Handbag House.

balearic pumping

Sound coming from any Ibizan toilet cubicle, usually after a paella.

trance
Short for 'I'm trying to dance'. Misheard
in noisy clubs, it became known as Trance. Dancing to trance is
really easy, cos you don't have to move your feet much.

acid trance
Short for 'I said, I'm
trying to dance!'. Variation on above, but found in noisier clubs.

techno
Something to do with expensive Lego
sets. Or computers. Actually, nobody knows where techno comes
from. Well, they might. But they haven't told us.

sash
Something to do with windows or Miss World.
We're not sure. But then nobody is, so we're not that worried.

chicane
Oh God, I dunno. Race cars?
Bollards? Bollocks most likely. I give up.

Steps

The Ibiza club scene's all about freedom of expression. Freedom to use your body as a tool of the music. It's anarchic spontaneous physical freeform. Anything goes as long as it comes from deep inside – a place connected with the texture of the rhythm. Mind you, get it even slightly wrong and you'll look a complete twat. If you've never larged it before, here's a few basic steps to get you started.

The Box

1 Shut your eyes
2 Mark out the shape of an imaginary box in front of you
3 Wrap it in a piece of imaginary paper
4 Fold the edges of the imaginary paper into a V at each end
5 Now stick the flaps down with imaginary sellotape
6 Hand the imaginary box to someone next to you (technically a separate dance called 'stacking boxes')

The Rope Climber

1 Shut your eyes
2 Grab hold of an imaginary rope hanging in front of you
3 Start to climb the imaginary rope (Note: if your feet leave the ground, this is not an imaginary rope. Check you're not in a playground.)
4 Once at the top, touch the imaginary ceiling
5 Slide down the imaginary rope
6 Look really hard cos your imaginary blisters don't hurt

The Karate Kid

1 Shut your eyes
2 Adopt the stance of Ralph Macchio, legendary teenage star of The Karate Kid movies (and that other crap one, where he played the guitar lots)
3 Paint an imaginary fence
4 Polish an imaginary car
5 Stand on one leg like an imaginary stork
6 Apologise to all the not imaginary people you just fell onto
7 Start again – maybe missing out the stork bit this time

never

1 Move your legs
2 Open your eyes
3 Stub cigarettes out on ladies' legs (sorry!)

Big Fish/Little Fish

1 I caught a fish THIS big
2 I caught a fish this big
3 I caught a fish THIS big
4 I caught a fish this big
5 Keep going 'til your arms ache and your fingers tingle

Curtains

1 Ooh, it's bedtime. I'd better close the curtains
2 Morning world. Time to open the curtains
3 Ooh, it's bedtime. I'd better close the curtains
4 Morning world. Time to open the curtains
5 Keep going 'til the curtain track breaks

becomin' a
monsta superstar

You might be going to Ibiza to dance and shag lots – which is OK I reckon, but if you're like me and Pel (i.e. definitely not virgins and very cool) you're actually goin' there cos you're dead wizard on the decks. You might be another Norman Cook (only not so bald) in which case Ibiza's the place to go to get your choons heard by the movers and the shakers in the record industry. Mind you, knowing your luck you'll probably just have your choons heard by the twitchers and jerkers in the record industry – and there's shed loads of them about, believe you me.

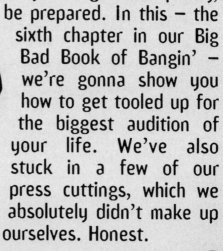

But if you really reckon you've got star quality, be prepared. In this – the sixth chapter in our Big Bad Book of Bangin' – we're gonna show you how to get tooled up for the biggest audition of your life. We've also stuck in a few of our press cuttings, which we absolutely didn't make up ourselves. Honest.

tools

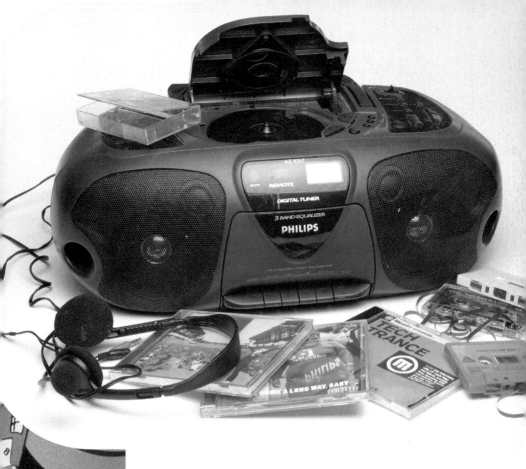

If you're gonna be a mixmeister, you need the right kit. Sadly, a twin deck mixing desk can be a bit spendy. Mind you, when you've only got £5.35 in the Post Office account your granny set up for you twelve years ago, anything's a bit spendy.

So what me and Kev have done is construct our own high-tech mixing equipment based on instructions we downloaded off the Internet. That's what we told Kev's Mum when the phone bill came in anyway.

DJ's
Kev & Pel
LARGIN' IT
@ THE ARNDALE

playing their
hit single

BiG GiRL

3pm Saturday
NO PARENTS!

giggin' it

The only way you're ever gonna make it big in the music business is if you start gettin' giggin' with it. That means taking your choons and playing them live to an appreciative and impressed audience. And there's no point trying to get out of it. If you can't play your choons live, you'll never make it as a DJ. But with the right attitude, and a bit of help from us, you'll have a stormer.

the venue

The most important thing about a gig is the location. Without a good venue, you might as well give up and go home. It's all very well setting up your decks in the middle of a field in Shropshire, and sending out secret rave invites on the internet to everyone you know, but if you've only got three mates, it'll go pants up.

The ideal venue is (i) free (ii) indoors (iii) full of people (iv) full of escape routes (v) far away from people who might recognise you.

After extensive research, we've come to the conclusion that your best bet is to set up in a shopping centre, pref'r'bly not in your home town where your PE teacher might see you and then take the piss during next day's lesson. But even this can have its problems.

timing

Tricky one this. Do you do the gig on a Saturday, when the shopping centre will be packed but you stand every chance of getting chucked out after thirty seconds? Or do you do it on a Thursday morning, when all the pensioners are loaded up with cash? Or maybe you should sneak in during the middle of the night and so avoid anyone actually seeing it?

We've worked out, after an in-depth study of all the gigs we've done that the absolute best time to do a gig is 4.35pm on a Wednesday afternoon. We did ours at 4.45pm, and quite frankly, it was crap. Ten minutes earlier, and we'd have had both those old ladies (and the four kids from our school) eating out of our hands instead of the plastic sandwich boxes they had with them from Marks & Spencer.

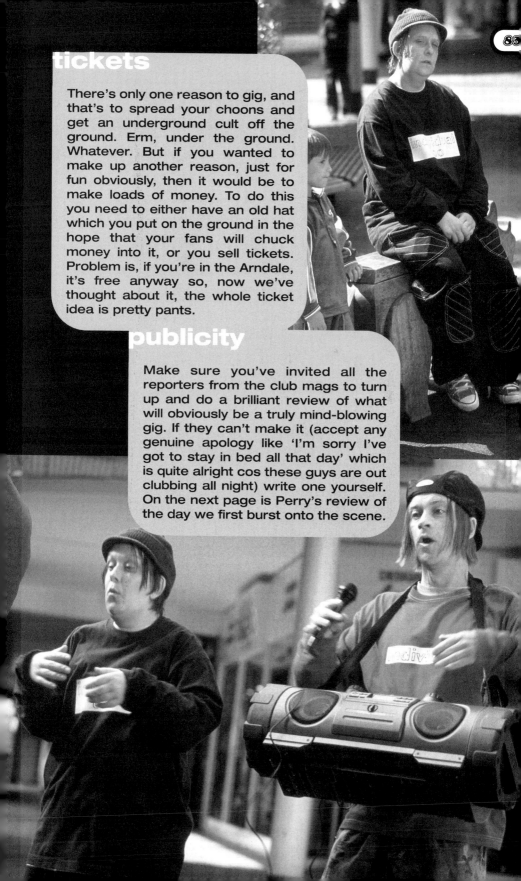

tickets

There's only one reason to gig, and that's to spread your choons and get an underground cult off the ground. Erm, under the ground. Whatever. But if you wanted to make up another reason, just for fun obviously, then it would be to make loads of money. To do this you need to either have an old hat which you put on the ground in the hope that your fans will chuck money into it, or you sell tickets. Problem is, if you're in the Arndale, it's free anyway so, now we've thought about it, the whole ticket idea is pretty pants.

publicity

Make sure you've invited all the reporters from the club mags to turn up and do a brilliant review of what will obviously be a truly mind-blowing gig. If they can't make it (accept any genuine apology like 'I'm sorry I've got to stay in bed all that day' which is quite alright cos these guys are out clubbing all night) write one yourself. On the next page is Perry's review of the day we first burst onto the scene.

KEV AND PEL STORM AT THE ARNDALE

Last Wednesday at the Arndale centre we saw the birth of two of the UK's most exciting new DJ talents. Not the real birth of course, that would have been quite messy, especially in a shopping precinct without any towels or hot water.

DJ Kev and DJ Pel are brilliant. Not just really good, which is what most DJs are, but really bloody brilliant. Their song 'Big Girl' is destined to be a monsta hit, mostly with the ladies who find the duo sexually irresistible. Although the gig started quietly – the batteries on Perry's stereo were a bit knackered so Kevin had to go and buy some more from Dixons – it kicked off as soon as two old ladies who sat down to eat their lunch 'seeded' the crowd.

Soon an enormous gathering of about seven or eight turned up, and the mall was thumpin'. The DJs whipped them into a frenzy, and they soon became too much for security to handle. Things came to a head when some girl Kevin said he'd shagged came up and called him a little wanker in front of everyone. Kev ran off and Perry had to pack the kit up. But it was still monsta.

DJ Kev and Pel will go far, depending which bus they catch.

interview
with DJ Kev & DJ Pel

Up and coming DJs Kev and Pel are really happenin'. Aren't we. They stormed Amnesia at this year's Ibiza with their debut white label 'Big Girl'. Using video samples from their own insider's tour of Ibiza, and some footage of Kev's Mum and Dad havin' it off, the track launched their fantastic careers into the stratosphere.

In this exclusive *MaxMig* interview we talk to the boyz, and find out what they're really like.

SO TELL ME KEVIN, WHY DID YOU WANT TO BE A DJ?
K: Because I'm immensely talented and I refuse to bow to the bourgeois career expectations of my fascist parents. And DJs get to shag more.

AND YOU PERRY?
P: For the shagging, definitely.

WHAT ARE YOUR INFLUENCES?
K: What, me?

YES, KEVIN.
K: Fatboy Slim, whose real name is Norman Cook I think you'll find, The Prodigy, obviously, and quite a lot of those CDs you get on the cover of *MaxMig*.

AND YOU PERRY?
P: Lorries reversin' mostly.

HOW COME YOU'RE BOTH SO FANTASTICALLY GOOD LOOKING AND IRRESISTIBLE TO THE LADIES?
K: I'll answer this one Perry. I think it's because we're both fantastically good looking, and consequently irresistible to the ladies.

WHO IS YOUR FAVOURITE DJ?
P: Chris Evans.
K: Shut up Perry!
P: Sorry Kev.
K: He didn't mean 'DJ'. God, you sound like my Dad!
P: I said I'm sorry Kev.
K: You make us sound like a couple of right bloody idiots!
P: Alright Kev, put a sock in it, OK?

LOOK, WILL YOU TWO STOP ARGUING?
P: Well he started it.
K: No I didn't. You're the one who thinks Chris Evans

is a DJ. The fact that me and him have both got ginger pubes doesn't make him a DJ. He's just not in my class.

P: No Kev, I'm the one in your class. Geography and Double Physics anyway.

CAN WE GET BACK TO THE INTERVIEW?

P: Only if Kevin apologises.

OH FOR GOODNESS SAKE...

K: Alright, alright. Sorry Pel (small sulk).

WHAT ARE YOUR PLANS FOR THE FUTURE?

K: Get Candice to lick my love pump.

P: And mine!!!

NO, I MEANT MUSICALLY...

K: Oh, right. Erm... bring out a second single. Do next year's Ibiza season at Amnesia. Headline at Glastonbury. Then the Reading Festival. Have a number one album. Sell-out nation-wide tour. Grand finale at Wembley Stadium. Go Triple-Platinum. Four number one hits off the album. Sell-out tour of Japan and the US. Bring out second album. Only get two hit singles. Do nationwide tour. Do US tour and come home half-way

through. Disappear for two years. Bring out third album which bombs. Get sacked by record company. Set up own label and bring out an experimental album. Go bankrupt. Sink into obscurity. Work in a record shop in Luton. Like most DJs really.

P: Learn the flute.

THANKS FOR YOUR TIME.

P: Do you want your car washed? Only two quid.

EVERY SATURDAY IN IBIZA

Eye Ball Paul

Advance tickets available from that dodgy looking tout by the ice cream shop.

ADVERTISEMENT PROMOTION

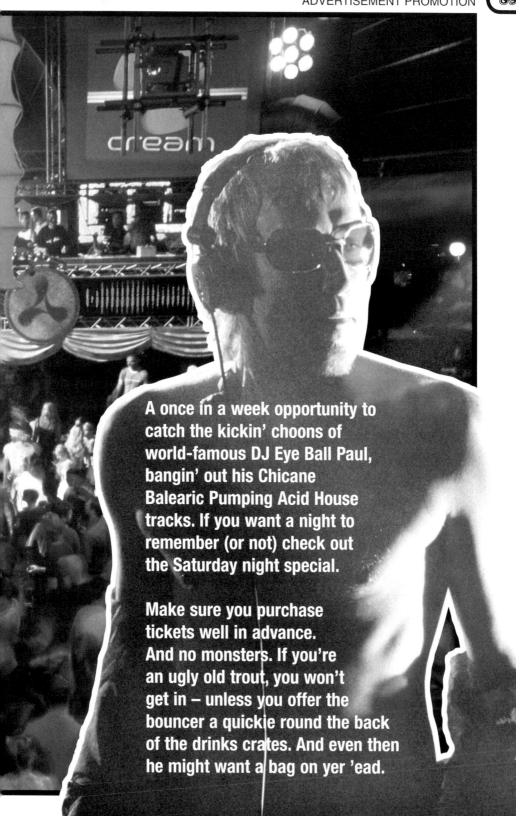

A once in a week opportunity to catch the kickin' choons of world-famous DJ Eye Ball Paul, bangin' out his Chicane Balearic Pumping Acid House tracks. If you want a night to remember (or not) check out the Saturday night special.

Make sure you purchase tickets well in advance. And no monsters. If you're an ugly old trout, you won't get in – unless you offer the bouncer a quickie round the back of the drinks crates. And even then he might want a bag on yer 'ead.

interview
with Eye Ball Paul

Eye Ball Paul is without doubt one of the greatest DJ phenomenas this summer. With his unique blend of Balearic Pumping Trance House Music, he has captivated the Ibiza scene like no other DJ since, well, last summer. We caught up with him after a set at Amnesia, where he presided over a night-long sesh that lasted until 6am, when the club closed. Like it always does at 6am.

COMPLETE THIS SENTENCE. EYE BALL PAUL IS...?
The dogs bollox.

DESCRIBE YOUR MUSIC IN THREE WORDS.
Big. Bad. Smelly.

GIVE ME TWO REASONS WHY I SHOULD PAY GOOD MONEY TO WATCH YOU PLAY?
Cos I'm the best. And my bouncers'll punch your lights out if you try and get in without paying.

EYE BALL PAUL'S TOP 15

1 **Nobby** – *Theme from Sticky Willy (Where Have You Bin?)* – Aftertaste (acetate) US
2 **Duff Muff** – *Keep Art of Ear* – Bigbuns (acetate) US
3 **Messy** – *Spinky Minky Munky Spunky (Original Mix)* – Aftertaste (bootleg) UK
4 **Messy** – *Spunky Minky Munky Spunky (Jism Mix)* – Aftertaste (bootleg) UK
5 **Messy** – *Spunky Munky Minky Spinky (Pants Mix)* – Aftertaste (bootleg) UK
6 **Messy** – *Spinky Munky Minky Spinky (Jam Rag Mix)* – Aftertaste (bootleg) UK
7 **Messy** – *Spinky Minky Minky Spinky (Spinky Mix)* – Aftertaste (bootleg) UK
8 **Messy** – *Spunky Munky Munky Spunky (Premature Mix)* – Aftertaste (bootleg) UK
9 **GX-90** – *gx-90* – GX-90 Germ
10 **Meat, Onions, Three Veg, Bit of Gravy** – *Soupkitchen* – Grubb Street (acetate) UK
11 **Derrick D C Concubine** – *Nubbin by Northwest* – Rusty Sheriff's Badge (remix) Newc.
12 **Cocks And Chicks** – *Hubble Bubble Double Trouble* – Pseudy Records UK
13 **DJ D.J. DeeJay** – *Gobble Me* – Madeuprecords (remix) US
14 **HairyNadge** – *Groovy Groovy Wup Wup* – Aftertaste (acetate) US
15 **Car Alarm** – *Car Alarm* – Halfords (£35.99) UK

WHAT ARE YOUR INFLUENCES?
Gary Glitter. Muffin the Mule. My beautiful body.

WHY DO THEY CALL YOU EYE BALL PAUL?
Cos I do this! *(sound of lid coming off vodka bottle, screaming)* Twat! Well 'ard, innit?

ER... RIGHT: TELL US A SECRET.
I've just nicked your wallet.

WHAT'S THE BEST PIECE OF ADVICE YOU'VE EVER GIVEN?
You can clean the shit out my toilet better if you get your arm in up to the elbow.

WHO ARE YOUR FRIENDS?
Friends are for tossers.

ARE YOU A COMPLETE TWAT?
I'm a DJ. And I've got more money than you. Who's the twat now?

THANKS EYE BALL PAUL.
Piss off!

ibiza!

7

introduction

Ibiza. The name itself conjures up images you've seen from loads of magazines... ladies, beaches, clubs, suitcases, erm, ladies. It's the party capital of the Mediterranean. So get clued up before you go or the days and nights will be wasted. Thank goodness me and Kev are your mates, cos we can give you the lowdown before you get there, and that's exactly what this chapter's all about.

For flip's sake, don't let your mate's parents know where the clubs are. They'll only hang around outside and wave at you when you come out, asking stupid questions like 'How was the disco, dear?' Or even worse, they'll try and get into the club to take you home. Thanks Mrs Patterson, that was <u>so</u> embarrassing! Your best bet's to keep this book stashed with your porno mags, and then they'll never find out. Although Mr Patterson might.

Ibiza! Rinsin'!
Large it!
Megaaaaaaaaa!

SPEAKA DA LINGO

Ibiza's one of those weirdy places that doesn't have its own language, but has instead nicked one from somewhere else – in this case Spain. Now you might think it a bit stupid havin' to talk another language on an island where everyone speaks English, but believe it or not, there's still some bolshy Spanish types who think you should talk their lardy-daa lingo.

We've knocked up a few essenshool phrases to make your holiday go with a bang.

Hello, my name is Kevin.
Hola me llamo Kevin.

Sausage, egg and chips please.
Salchichas con huevos fritos y patas fritas, por favour.

Two beers please.
Dos cervezas por favor.

Yes, of course I'm eighteen.
Claro que tengo diez y ocho años.

Where do the pretty ladies go to snog DJs?
¿A dónde van las guapas parar enrollarse con los Disc Jockeys?

Where's the beach?
¿Dónde esta la playa?

My mate fancies your mate.
A mi amigo le gusta tu amiga.

We're friends of the DJ.
Somos amigos del DJ.

No, honest, he's my best friend.
No, de verdad, es mi mejor amigo.

Get your hands off my jacket!
¡Suelta la jaqueta!

Owww!
¡Ow!

Perry, I think I've cut my lip.
Perry, creo que me sale sangre por los labios.

Bastard.
¡Bastardo!

Hello lady, are you Spanish?
¿Hola señora, eres Español?

Will you lick my love plank?
¿Quieres lamer mi palo de amor?

CAUTION:
You will blow any credibility you may have by pronouncing Ibiza wrong.
RIGHT – I beefah
WRONG – Eye-bitz-ia

Unless you want to spend your entire holiday getting lifts off your parents (and then you'll <u>never</u> get a shag!), or spending your entire allowance on stinky Spanish taxis, you'll need some transport. And nothing suits up-and-coming DJs (or impresses the ladies) more than a couple of mega-trendy Vespa scooters.

Unfortunately, there's only four mega-trendy Vespa scooters on the entire island. The rest of the bikes have been knocked together out of discarded spare parts and bits of metal off the beach. Learning how to stay in control is a bit tricky, but in the interests of research, me and Kevin crashed ours lots to find out the best way to drive them.

Here's some essenshool information on Ibiza's bike scene.

bein' mobile

hiring

Never take the first bike Manuel offers you. He'll always try to shift the really crappy one first. Ask him to drive it around before you hire it. If he laughs, choose another. If he goes white and disappears out the back, go somewhere else.

petrol

You'll be given the bike with about an egg-cup of petrol in it, which means it'll run out the moment you've left town, and a bloody long way from the nearest petrol station. You'll be expected to fill it up before it's returned.

crash helmets

Obviously wearing a helmet makes you look like a complete tool. Unfortunately you stand even less chance of having a shag if you've left half your brains over some Ibizan pavement piazza. You'll need one. Make sure it's not made of cardboard, or egg boxes.

maps

Ibiza's such a small island, you won't need a map. Until you get lost that is. Then ask a local for directions. Go the exact opposite way they tell you.

highway code

On hiring the bike, you'll be given a copy of Ibiza's highway code, usually printed on the back of a playing card. Ignore it. Basic rules are as follows:

- All trucks will try to knock down all cars
- All cars will try to knock down all bikes
- All bikes will try to knock down all pedestrians

Try and go with the flow.

Nice looking helmet!

Whisper instructions here.

Pointy ones are more aerodynamic.

A firm grip (in a soft glove!) is really important.

In emergency grab elastic.

Sit here.

Avoid exhaust.

Keep your hands here for maximum comfort.

Keep eyes fixed here.

using your bike

Here's a picture of a perfect moped – complete with automatic pilot. It's by far the best way to get a ride. Mmmm...

places to

There's loads of places to go once you get to Ibiza. Luckily, they're quite a bit like the places we hang around in England. Check 'em out!

Park benches – plenty of these in Ibiza. If you can't get in the nightclub, sit on one of these all night.

visit in ibiza

Brilliant! Looks like a bus stop. <u>IS</u> a bus stop! Good place to meet girls. Well, ones waiting for a bus anyway.

Fast food shops – you can eat AND meet your friends. Monsta!

Joe's Cafe (seafront)

Ann's Cafe (seafront)

Perfect energy food after a good night's shagging on the beach!

Maureen's Cafe (seafront)

Eggs a bit runny, like my bottom.

Mick's Cafe (seafront)

Ibiza's most famous beach – The Beach – can get very crowded, especially after Amnesia chucks out. We've counted and there are 8,728 boobies in this picture.

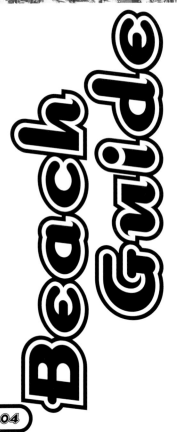

Beach Guide

Ibiza's famous 'Stiffy Tower.'

After a long night's clubbing, many ravers retire to the beach and prise off their trainers. It can take several hours for all the cheese to fall off and dissolve.

In their spare time, many club bouncers run donkey rides on Ibiza's beaches. But watch out – if you're a monster or nearly dead like my fascist parents, they won't let you on.

The Ten Commandments of Havin' It Large

1. Thou shalt not fart when thou art sitting next to thou's best mate on a plane.

2. Thou shalt wear thy puffa always, even when thou art on the beach and getting bloody hot.

3. Thou shalt never dance with the Germans, who art easily spotted by their mullet haircuts and crap shirts.

4. Thou shalt never go up to the DJ and ask him to play 'Tragedy' by Steps, which makes thou look crappy and means thou will never shag.

5. Thou shalt never poo in thou's pants when thou art swimming, for it may be a floater.

6. Thou shalt never speak to thine parents, who are there to ruin thine's holiday.

7. If thou art stupid enough to be seen in public with thine parents, call them by their first names, in case there art any ladies listening and who might think thou art a complete saddo for going on holiday with thine's parents. (Oh, and it really irritates them as well, which is another good reason for doing it.)

8. Thou shalt never eat any local rubbish. Stick to thine's good old egg, sausage and chips.

9. Thou shalt never go home before 7am, unless thine runs out of money, in which case thou should nip back to the apartment and scrounge some off thine fascist parents who are really selfish and keep it all for themselves.

10. Thou shalt never vomit on thyself when a bit squiffy. Find a German instead.

DEALING
— WITH A —
TEENAGER

A PRACTICAL GUIDE TO
ADOLESCENT EXORCISM

Mr & Mrs Patterson

CHAPTER
ONE

It is a little known fact that there is a parallel universe which sits alongside our own. This universe is exactly the same as ours, except that all of their children are evil, twisted, hateful, vicious, uncaring, aggressive little idiots. When our children reach the age of thirteen, an alien spacecraft comes along and takes them away and puts one of these twisted freaks in their place. At the age of eighteen they swap them back again.

For five, dreadful, awful years, we have to deal with psychotic teenagers from another dimension. As parents who have been through this, we wrote this book to offer help and solace to others in the same situation. Those who might genuinely be weighing up the price of life imprisonment just so they can have the pleasure of bludgeoning their teenagers to death.

Communication

Shouting

Shouting is the preferred form of communication for all teenagers. This is punctuated by slamming doors and stomping up stairs.

Do not rise to the bait. Your average teenager is just looking for a fight so he can then call you a fascist for trying to impose some semblance of humanity in your household. Ignore him, and eventually he'll go away (it takes about another four or five years, but it's worth waiting for).

The Contemptuous Sneer

Not strictly a form of communication – more a state of mind. To understand your teenager, you need to grasp how he sees you. To him you are a nobody. You know nothing. Have done nothing. You're stupid. You were never young, and if you were, you were a useless person even then. Don't try to disavow him of this idea. Playing Oasis records and wearing Caterpillar trainers will only infuriate him more.

Sulking

When they're not shouting, the natural state of repose for your average teenager is the sulk. The intensity of the sulk can often be severe enough for individual weather patterns to appear over the teenager's head – usually a black cloud with lightning and thunderbolts.

It is impossible to break through the sulk unless you make a specific reference to (i) staying in tonight (ii) reducing pocket money (iii) asking them to clear up their room. All other attempts at communication will not be understood.

The Grizzle

Occasionally, when some tragedy befalls your teenager that had nothing to do with you (getting chucked, falling out with their best friend, etc.) a glimmer of normality will return to your teenager's personality. However, this 'normality' recalls the emotional incontinence of an eight-year-old. There will be extensive wailing and tears. In circumstances such as this, treat him like an eight-year-old – offer to play Scalectrix, take him fishing or buy him some sweets.

Be warned however. This state will last no more than four hours at most. Be prepared for an enormous backlash when he snaps out of it. Now you will be blamed for the original calamity, and any other vague crimes that he might be able to pin on you.

The Teenager's Room

1 Degrading poster of scantily-clad bimbo. Essential – remove at your own risk.

2 Inflatable Alien – no-one knows why.

3 En-suite toilet. Not a luxury, a necessity. Never, ever, go in there.

4 Clothes. The wardrobe is used to store pornographic magazines. This leaves no room for clothes, which must fester for at least six months before you're allowed to peel them off the carpet.

we're night-clubbing

ntroduction

This is it. The bit you came for. Well, this and the shagging afterwards. But unless you get it right in the club, the shag'll never happen.

To the virgin, a club can be an intimidating and scary experience. As top DJ mixmeisters, me an' Pel have always felt at home in the subterranean culture of dance and clubbing. (But then we also feel equally at home hanging around bus-stops and being a menace in the shopping precinct.)

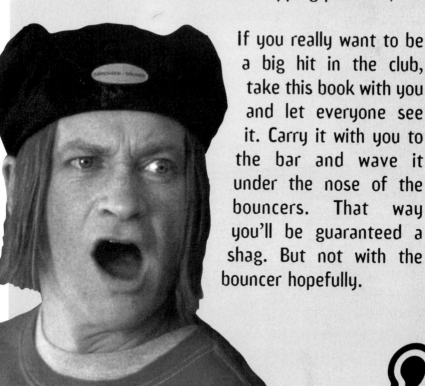

If you really want to be a big hit in the club, take this book with you and let everyone see it. Carry it with you to the bar and wave it under the nose of the bouncers. That way you'll be guaranteed a shag. But not with the bouncer hopefully.

the club

HERE'S THE ESSENSHOOL GUIDE TO
GETTIN' IN THE CLUB, AND HAVIN' A
RINSIN' TIME ONCE YOU'RE THERE!

THE BOUNCER

DO SAY: I'm a mate of Eye Ball Paul. We're on the list. Cheers mate.

DON'T SAY: Oh go on, please, pleeeeeease. I'm desperate for a shag. Just let me go in and have a look. Ow, that hurts! Ow! I'm gonna get my Dad!

BUYING A DRINK

DO SAY: Two Dead Bulls and Vodka.

DON'T SAY: Are you allowed to buy alcohol if you're under 18 in Ibiza? Are you sure? OK... I'll have one of those pink ones. With an umbrella in it.

GETTING INTO THE VIP LOUNGE

DO SAY: Can you believe it? Bloody Norman's forgotten his choons again. Would you make sure none of these losers see me? I'll never get out again if they know DJ (your name here) is doing a set.

DON'T SAY: Is that Paul Van Dyk over there? I know his dog trainer. Well, my Mum knows his dog trainer. I cleared some cat shit off his carpet once.

DANCING

DO: Turn to page 74 for our monsta tips on the *only* moves you should be doing on the floor (apart from with the ladies of course – hur hur! – Pel).

DON'T: Sit on the floor trying to get a 'rowing' dance formation going with your mates from Bristol.

TALKING TO LADIES

DO: Turn to page 46 before you even think about approaching one.

DON'T: Even think about approaching the ladies before reading page 46. Or you'll regret it. Seriously.

VOMITING

If you need to chunder, do it in the toilets or in the alley down the side of the club. NOT on girls or barstaff. Under no circumstances snog a lady after barfing. They hate it, apparently.

LEAVING

DO SAY: I'm doin' another set at Cream tonight. My driver's about to pick me up.

DON'T SAY: Oh shit. Is that the time? My Dad's gonna kill me... Can I borrow a fiver for a taxi?

drugs
are
for
losers

You don't need drugs to have a good time. In fact, you can have a better time without them. And you can have an even better time when other people don't take them, and then puke all over your head while you're dancing to rinsin' choons, innit.

fags

Believe it or not, fags are drugs. And pretty crappy ones at that. They stink, they burn holes in your puffa, and your Dad always ends up nicking them.

cannabis

All cannabis is smuggled into the country up someone's arse, which is why it always looks, smells and tastes of turd.

es

Es are made from treated sewage and other stuff. The picture on the side tells you what's in it. White doves for instance, have dried birds' intestines (or worse, dried cows' intestines), and Mitsubishis are made from manky engine oil. Take more than three, and you lose the ability to blink for the rest of your life. This makes your eyeballs dry up and fall out.

Oil

coke

Coke (or Beechams) is always mixed with Flea Powder and Caustic soda to give a bigger 'hit'. But it melts your nose and your face collapses after two or three hits. One line of coke costs about £300.

the ladies.

There are many different types of lady in a club. It helps if you can spot which one is which before you make an idiot of yourself. Although knowing which one is which doesn't always stop you making an idiot of yourself. Does it Perry?

the babe

This is the holy grail of all club ladies. She's horny, she wants it, and she dances so well you'll have a permanent stiffy. Sadly, they are very tricky to get off with. Which means you often end up trying to hit on the...

monster

If she's lucky enough to get past the bouncers – who don't usually let real trogs into the club – the monster is the last hope for the holiday shag. Usually a complete pushover, except most Monsters have a best friend who's a Babe. And that can make getting off with her almost as tricky as the Babe itself, sorry, herself.

the frigisaurus

She's old, she's got a face like an alligator handbag and she'll wave her old lady tits in your face and pretend she fancies you. Then when you so much as look at her she'll laugh and walk off.

the herdivore

Herdivores travel in packs, giggling amongst themselves and whispering to each other so you can't hear them. Never try and talk to a herdivore, as you'll end up addressing the entire herd, and if one doesn't like you, none of them will like you.

the rottweiler

Not a bad looker, but the Rottweiler is the scariest lady on the planet. Even the most friendly of approaches will be met by a snarl that would scare the pants off Bruce Willis. Stay away.

the trance tart

Doesn't matter what you do – stand in front of her, shout, wave your arms, let off a thermonuclear bomb. The trance tart is away with the fairies. And quite frankly, they're welcome to her.

photo
album

Candice & Gemma
(we shagged 'em
LARGE!)

Perry - gettin' eyed
up by two ladies
on the beach

Best mates!

Perry about to
attempt the two-times
'Yawn & Grab'

Big Girl! Big Girl!

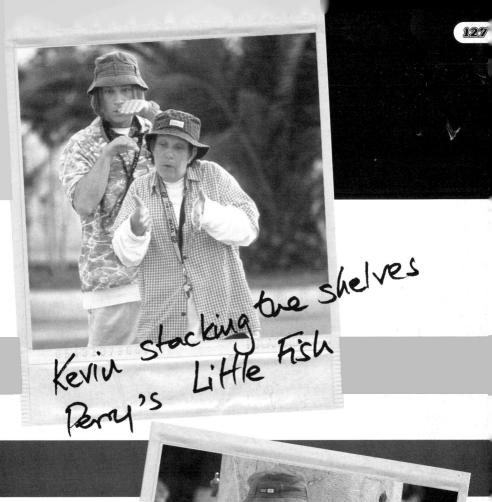

Kevin stacking the shelves
Perry's Little Fish

Kev, with a dog he met
at Amnesia.

You've read the book, now buy the album!

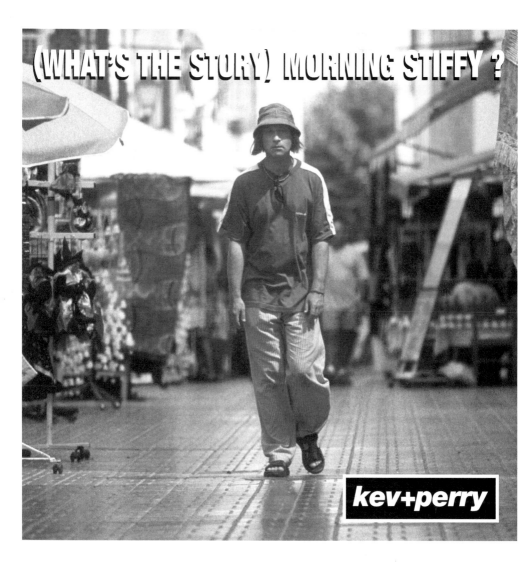

(WHAT'S THE STORY) MORNING STIFFY ?

kev+perry

Includes DJs Kev & Pel's hit singles:

Don't Look Back at Ongar

Wonderwally

Cigarettes and Alcohol (got any?)

IN SHOPS NOW